Contents

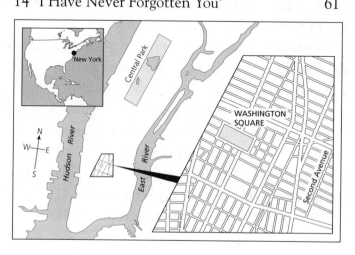

A Note About the Author

Henry James was born in New York City on 15th April 1843. His father was a lecturer and he wrote about religion. His brother was a philosopher.

Henry James studied in New York, London, Paris, Boulogne and Geneva. From 1862, he studied law at Harvard University. But he never worked as a lawyer.

In the 1860s, Henry started writing short stories for magazines. In 1875, Henry lived in Paris. His friends were the writers Ivan Turgenev and Gustave Flaubert.

In 1876, Henry James came to Britain. He lived in London. One of his famous friends was H.G. Wells – the science fiction writer. In 1898, Henry moved from London. He lived in a house in Rye – a town by the sea, in the southern county of Sussex.

Henry James was a busy writer. He wrote magazine articles, short stories, plays and travel stories. And he wrote more than twenty novels. Many of his stories are about Americans. But many of these Americans visit Europe, or live there. Some of these stories are: *The American* (1877), *Washington Square* (1880), *Portrait of a Lady* (1881), *The Bostonians* (1886), *What Maisie Knew* (1897), *The Turn of the Screw* (1898), *The Wings of a Dove* (1902) and *The Ambassadors* (1903).

In 1915, Henry became British. He had lived in Britain for 39 years. He loved the country and the people. He wanted to be a citizen of Britain. The next year, Henry James received an award – the Order of Merit – from King George V.

Henry James died in London on 28th February 1916. He was 73 years old.

A Note About This Story

Time: 1847 to 1866. **Place:** New York City.

At this time, Washington Square, in the centre of New York City, was quiet and there were many trees. Rich people lived in large houses there. They had many servants and they rode in carriages. Fine horses pulled these carriages.

a carriage

There are films of many of Henry James' stories. There have been two films of this story – 'The Heiress' (1949) and 'Washington Square' (1997).

The People in This Story

Doctor Austin Sloper
'dɒktə(r) 'ɒstan 'sləʊpə(r)

Miss Catherine Sloper
mɪs 'cæθrən 'sləʊpə(r)

Mrs Lavinia Penniman
'mɪsɪz lə'vɪnɪə 'penimæn

Mrs Elizabeth Almond
'mɪsɪz ɪl'ɪzabəθ 'ɑːmənd

Miss Marian Almond
mɪs 'mærɪan ɑːmənd

Arthur Townsend
'ɑː(r)θə' taʊnsend

Morris Townsend
'mɒrɪs taʊnsend

Mrs Mary Montgomery
'mɪsɪz 'meəri mɒnt'gʌməri

6

The House in Washington Square

Austin Sloper lived in New York City. He lived in a house in Washington Square. Washington Square was in a fashionable part of the city. Austin Sloper was a rich and clever man. He was a doctor.

Catherine Sloper lived with her father in the big red house. Catherine's mother was dead – Doctor Austin Sloper was a widower. But the doctor had two sisters. His younger sister, Mrs Lavinia Penniman, was a widow – her husband was dead. Mrs Penniman lived in the house in Washington Square too.

Catherine Sloper was a kind young woman. She loved her father, but she did not understand him. Doctor Sloper was not a happy man. He had loved his clever, beautiful wife. But he did not love his daughter.

'Catherine is not beautiful,' the doctor often said to himself. 'And she is not clever. Nobody will marry her. Who wants a plain, uninteresting wife?'

The Party at Mrs Almond's House

Doctor Sloper's older sister was Mrs Elizabeth Almond. One afternoon in January 1847, Mrs Almond visited Doctor Sloper's house in Washington Square. She talked to her sister, Lavinia, and to Catherine.

'My daughter, Marian, is engaged to be married,' Mrs Almond said. 'She is going to marry Arthur Townsend. Arthur is a fine young man. He has a very good job. I will give an engagement party for them next week. Please come to the party.'

'Thank you, Aunt Elizabeth,' Catherine said. 'We will all come to the party.'

That evening, Lavinia Penniman was excited. She talked to Catherine about the engagement party.

'There will be many young men at the party, Catherine,' she said. 'You must buy a new dress.'

Catherine Sloper was not beautiful. But she liked fashionable clothes. She bought a new silk dress for the party. The dress was bright red, with gold decorations.

———

It was the evening of the engagement party. Catherine and her Aunt Lavinia were standing in the hall of the house in Washington Square. They were looking at themselves in a big mirror. They were both wearing new clothes.

Catherine's father came down the stairs.

'Well, my dear!' Doctor Sloper said to Catherine. 'Your dress is very fine. It's very – rich! Everybody will like your dress. Enjoy yourself, my dear. I will see you later, at your aunt's house.'

Half an hour later, Catherine and her Aunt Lavinia were at Marian's engagement party. There were many young people in the large room. Some of them were Marian's friends and some of them were Arthur Townsend's friends. Most of the young people were dancing.

Catherine and Mrs Penniman sat down. Catherine looked around her. After a few moments, Marian Almond came over to her. A tall young man was walking beside Marian. He was very handsome. Marian introduced the tall young man to her cousin.

'Catherine, this is Mr Morris Townsend. He is my dear Arthur's cousin,' said Marian. 'Mr Townsend wants to meet you, my dear.'

Catherine smiled at Morris Townsend, but she did not speak. The young man bowed.

'I'm happy to meet you,' he said. 'This is a very good party. But why aren't you dancing, Miss Sloper? Will you dance with me?'

Catherine still said nothing. But she smiled again and she stood up. The two young people began to dance. Suddenly Catherine was very happy!

After the dance, Catherine was very warm. Her face was red.

'You are tired, Miss Sloper,' Morris Townsend said. 'Look! Here is a seat for two people. We will sit here and we will talk.'

The two young people sat down. Morris Townsend talked and Catherine listened.

'Mr Townsend is very handsome!' Catherine thought. 'And he talks well too. He is very clever and interesting. And he is talking to *me*!'

There were many people in the room. But Catherine was only looking at Morris Townsend.

Then Marian Almond came towards them. She spoke quietly to her cousin.

'Catherine,' she said, 'I must take Mr Townsend away now. My mother wants to speak to him.'

Morris Townsend stood up.

'We will meet again soon, Miss Sloper,' he said.

Half an hour later, Catherine was dancing with one of Marian's brothers. She saw Morris Townsend talking to her Aunt Lavinia. Mrs Penniman was smiling. Sometimes they looked towards her. Were they talking about her? Catherine did not know. But she was very happy. Then suddenly, she saw her father watching her. Doctor Sloper smiled at his daughter. Soon, the music stopped and the dance finished. The doctor walked over to her.

'Who is this fine young lady?' the doctor said. 'Is she my daughter? She is lovely. And her clothes are very fashionable – very rich. Yes! She *is* my daughter! Have you enjoyed the party, my dear?'

'Yes, Father,' Catherine replied. 'But I am tired. I want to go home now, please.'

Catherine was *not* tired. But she did want to go

home. She wanted to be alone in her room. And she wanted to think about Morris Townsend.

———

Catherine, Mrs Penniman and Doctor Sloper went home in the doctor's carriage. In the carriage, Doctor Sloper talked to his sister.

'I saw you talking to a handsome young man, Lavinia,' the doctor said. 'What were you two talking about?'

'We were talking about Catherine,' Mrs Penniman replied.

'Oh! Aunt Lavinia!' Catherine said.

'Is the young man in love with Catherine?' Doctor Sloper asked. He laughed. 'Her clothes are very – rich. Yes, the young man is in love with her.' He laughed again.

'Oh, Father!' Catherine said. 'That isn't true! But he was a very interesting young man. *I* talked to him too.'

'And what is this interesting young man's name?' the doctor asked.

Suddenly, Catherine's face became hot and red. But it was dark inside the carriage. Doctor Sloper could not see his daughter's face clearly.

'I don't know his name, Father,' she replied.

Her father believed her. This was her first lie to him.

3

Morris Townsend

A few days after the engagement party, Morris Townsend visited the house in Washington Square. He came with his cousin, Arthur. Doctor Sloper was not at home. Arthur talked to Catherine and Morris talked to her Aunt Lavinia.

'Morris wanted to come here,' Arthur Townsend told Catherine. 'Your Aunt Lavinia invited him. She wrote him a letter. Morris wants to meet people in New York. He has been away from the city for a long time. He has travelled round the world.'

'My aunt likes him very much,' Catherine said. 'He is a very clever young man. Is he going to stay in New York now?'

'I don't know, Miss Sloper,' Arthur said. 'His sister and her family live here, in the city. He has no other relations. Morris is living at his sister's house and he is trying to find a job.'

Catherine looked across the room at Morris. 'He is very handsome,' she thought. And at that moment, Morris turned away from Mrs Penniman and looked towards her.

'We were talking about you, Morris,' Arthur told his cousin.

Morris smiled.

'And I have been talking about *you*, Miss Sloper,' he said. 'I have been learning about you from your aunt. Arthur and I must go now. But I will come again. Then we will talk together.'

The two young men bowed and they left the room.

'What did Mr Townsend say about me?' Catherine asked her aunt. 'What did you tell him? Why did he come here?'

Mrs Penniman laughed.

'I invited that young man,' she said. 'But he did not want to talk to me. He wanted to talk to you, Catherine. He likes you very much, my dear.'

'But he doesn't know me,' Catherine said. 'And we don't know him.'

'That's true,' her aunt replied. 'But I have told him all about you.' She smiled happily. 'And he will come again soon!'

———

In the evening, Doctor Sloper came home.

'Mr Morris Townsend has been here, Austin,' his sister told him.

'Mr Morris Townsend?' the doctor said. 'Who is Mr Morris Townsend?'

'He was at the Almonds' party, Father,' Catherine said quietly. 'You asked me about him in the carriage. I could not remember his name then.'

'Ah, yes,' said the doctor. 'So, the young man's name is Morris Townsend! Why did he come here? Does he want you to marry him, Catherine?' He laughed.

Catherine did not answer. She walked over to the window. She put her face against the cold glass and she looked out into the street.

'I want to meet your friend, Mr Townsend,' Doctor Sloper said. Then he left the room.

———

Soon, Morris Townsend visited the big red house in Washington Square. Again, Doctor Sloper was not at home. Mrs Penniman was in the house, but Catherine talked to the young man alone in the sitting-room. Morris stayed for a long time. He asked Catherine many questions about herself. Then he looked into her eyes and he smiled.

'Miss Sloper, I like talking to you,' he said. 'We both like the same things. We both like music. We both like going to the theatre. We don't read many books. You are honest and kind, Miss Sloper. I like you very much.'

Catherine did not speak, but she was very happy. This handsome young man was talking about *her*. And he liked her very much!

———

That evening, Catherine spoke to her father.

'Mr Morris Townsend came here again today, Father,' she said.

'Well?' he said. 'Does he want you to marry him, Catherine?' The doctor laughed.

After a moment, Catherine laughed too.

'No, Father,' she said. 'Not this week. He didn't ask me today.'

Then Catherine smiled at her father and she left the room quickly.

Doctor Sloper was very surprised. Was his daughter in love? Suddenly, the doctor was worried. He went to Mrs Almond's house and he spoke to his older sister.

'Elizabeth, what do you know about Morris Townsend?' the doctor asked.

'Lavinia asked me that question, Austin,' Mrs Almond replied. 'I don't know very much about him. He lives with his sister. Her name is Mrs Montgomery and she lives on Second Avenue. Morris hasn't got a job. One of his relations died and gave him some money. But now he has spent all that money.'

'He has visited Catherine several times,' Doctor Sloper said. 'Why? Catherine is twenty-two years old and no young men want to know her. There are many beautiful, interesting young women in New York. But Catherine isn't interesting and she isn't beautiful.'

'She will be rich one day, Austin,' said Mrs Almond. 'And rich girls always get married.'

Doctor Sloper looked at his sister for a moment. Then he laughed quietly.

'Ah!' he said. 'Does Mr Townsend want Catherine or does he want her money? Please give me his sister's address, Elizabeth.'

———

A week later, Doctor Sloper gave a dinner party at the house in Washington Square. He invited Morris Townsend. At the party, the doctor watched the young man carefully.

'Townsend is clever,' the doctor said to himself. 'He

likes talking. He likes my good food and my fine wine too. And he's very handsome. But I don't like him!'

After the meal, Morris talked quietly with Catherine.

'Your father doesn't like me, Miss Sloper,' he said.

'Why do you say that, Mr Townsend?' Catherine replied. 'My father doesn't know you.'

Morris smiled. But he was not happy about Catherine's answer. He looked at Doctor Sloper.

Austin Sloper was watching the two young people carefully. He was worried.

'No. I do not like Morris Townsend,' he said to himself again. 'I will find out more about him.'

4

Morris Is Angry

Morris Townsend visited the house in Washington Square three or four times every week. He always spoke to Catherine alone. Sometimes he met Mrs Penniman for a few minutes. But Doctor Sloper was never at home.

Catherine was very happy. But she did not tell anybody about her happiness. She did not speak to her father about Morris Townsend. And she did not speak to her aunt about the young man.

One evening, Doctor Sloper visited his older sister's house. Catherine and Morris Townsend were there too. They were sitting together and talking quietly. The doctor watched them carefully.

'Catherine is very plain and the young man is very handsome,' he thought. 'She loves him. She is going to be very unhappy.'

Later in the evening, Doctor Sloper saw Morris Townsend standing alone in front of the fire. Suddenly, the doctor walked over to the young man and started talking to him.

'Have you found a job in New York City, young man?' Doctor Sloper asked.

'Why do you ask, sir?' Morris replied. 'Do you have a job for me?'

'No. I don't have a job for you!' the doctor said.

'Are you going to stay in the city?'

'Yes,' Morris replied. 'My sister and her children live here. I teach the children Spanish.'

'But you are not earning any money,' Doctor Sloper said.

'That's true,' said Morris. 'I'm not a rich man.'

'I know that,' said the doctor. 'But I *am* a rich man. Please don't think about *my* money, Mr Townsend!'

Morris Townsend was very angry. Quickly, he found Catherine and he spoke to her.

'I want you to meet me tomorrow, Miss Sloper,' he said. 'I must speak to you about something important. But I will not come to Washington Square.'

Catherine looked at the young man. She was very surprised.

'What is wrong, Mr Townsend?' she asked. 'Are you ill? And why won't you come to our house tomorrow?'

'Your father has insulted me, Miss Sloper,' Morris replied. 'I am a poor man. But I am a proud man too. I will not come to your house again.'

'I am afraid of my father, but you are my friend, Mr Townsend,' Catherine said. 'You must come to our house. You must come!'

'Very well,' Morris replied. 'I will come tomorrow afternoon. Your father will not be at home then.'

And he walked away.

5

The Engagement

The next afternoon, Morris Townsend came to the house in Washington Square. In the hall, he spoke to Mrs Penniman for a few moments. But he wanted to see Catherine alone.

Lavinia Penniman was very excited.

'He wants her to marry him,' she thought. 'He is going to ask her about it today.' She smiled at Morris.

'Please go into the sitting-room, Mr Townsend,' she said. 'Catherine is waiting for you.'

Morris stood in front of the mirror in the hall for a moment. He looked at his fashionable clothes. Then he opened the sitting-room door and he went in.

Catherine was standing by the window. Morris walked across to her. He held both her hands in his hands for a moment.

'Catherine,' he said. 'My dear girl. I love you. I love you very much.'

At first, Catherine did not speak. Morris put his arms around her and he kissed her. He kissed her again. And then he kissed her a third time.

'Oh, Morris! Is this true?' Catherine said. 'Do you love me?'

'Yes, Catherine, I love you,' Morris replied. 'And I want to marry you.'

Catherine looked up at the tall, handsome young man.

'What will my father say?' Catherine said. 'We must tell him about our love. I will speak to him tonight. And you must speak to him tomorrow.'

Morris smiled.

'You are very brave, my dear,' he said. 'But you must be careful. Your father will not be happy about this news. I am a poor man. Your family is rich. Your father will tell you, "Morris Townsend wants your money!" He will say bad things about me.'

'He will be wrong!' Catherine replied. 'I will change his mind. You must not worry about money, Morris. We will get married soon. I have some money from my mother. One day, I will have my father's money too. Then we will both be rich. We will be very happy, my dear.'

'Yes, we will be happy,' Morris said.

Catherine turned away from Morris and looked out of the window. For a moment, she did not speak. Then she said, 'Do you love me Morris? Are you sure about that?'

'Yes, Catherine,' Morris replied. 'I will always love you. And you must always love me. Your father will be angry with us. But please, don't change your mind, my dear.'

'Oh, Morris,' Catherine said.

And the handsome young man kissed her hand.

———

In the evening, Doctor Sloper came home. He went into his library and closed the door behind him. Catherine sat alone in the sitting-room for half an hour. Then she stood up and she walked to the door of the library. She knocked on the door and she went in.

'Father, I must tell you something. It's something important,' she said.

The doctor did not reply. Catherine waited for a moment, then she spoke again.

'I am engaged, Father,' she said. 'I am going to be married!'

'Who is the happy man?' the doctor asked quietly.

'Mr Morris Townsend,' Catherine replied. 'He will speak to you about it tomorrow.'

'When did this engagement happen?' the doctor asked.

'About two hours ago, Father,' said Catherine.

'You have known Mr Townsend for a very short time, my dear,' Doctor Sloper said quietly. Then suddenly, his voice was angry. 'Catherine, I don't like this engagement. Why didn't you speak to me about Mr Townsend's plans?'

'I was afraid, Father,' Catherine replied. 'You don't like Morris. You told me that. But I want you to like him. You don't know him, and I *do* know him!'

'No, Catherine,' the doctor said. 'No. You *don't* know Mr Townsend. He is a very clever young man. You are kind and honest. You do not understand him. He doesn't love you. He loves your money. He will spend it very quickly. He has spent all his own money and now he wants to spend your money too!'

'You are wrong, Father,' Catherine said. 'Morris is a kind man. And he loves me.'

'I don't believe it!' Doctor Sloper said coldly. 'But I will speak to Mr Townsend about this tomorrow.'

6

Letters and Arguments

The next afternoon, Morris Townsend visited Doctor Sloper at Washington Square. Catherine and her aunt were not at home. The doctor spoke first.

'I do not like this engagement,' Doctor Sloper said. 'I do not want you to be my son-in-law. You are a young man without a job and without money. My daughter is rich. One day she will be richer. But she is a weak young woman. She doesn't know much about life. And she doesn't understand clever young men!'

Morris replied quietly.

'Your daughter is not weak, sir,' he said. 'You do not understand her. She is kind, but she is strong. Catherine loves me. I am poor. That is true. But I love her. I love your daughter, sir. Can't you believe me?'

'I don't *want* to believe you,' the doctor replied.

'Do you want to make Catherine unhappy?' Morris asked angrily.

'She will be unhappy for a few months,' the doctor said. 'But she won't be your wife. Your wife will be unhappy all her life!'

Morris was very, very angry.

'You are not polite, sir!' he shouted. 'But Catherine will always love me and I will always love her. Goodbye, Doctor Sloper!'

Morris Townsend quickly left the house.

Doctor Sloper smiled.

'They are both afraid of me,' he said to himself. 'That is good! Catherine will not marry him.'

The doctor went to the desk in his library. He sat down and he wrote a letter to Morris Townsend's sister.

Washington Square

February, 1847

Dear Mrs Montgomery,

Your brother wants to marry my daughter.
But he has no job and no money. One
day, my daughter will be very rich.
Your brother wants to marry Catherine
for her money.

I want to tell you something. Catherine
has some money from her mother. I can't
do anything about that. But your
brother will never get my money. I
shall give all my money to a hospital.
I will tell your brother that. Then he
will change his mind about this
engagement.

Your brother is clever and handsome.
But I do not like him. And I do
not want him to be my son-in-law.

Yours sincerely,

Doctor Austin Sloper

Mrs Montgomery replied to the letter the next day. Her reply was short.

Second Avenue

February – 1847

Dear Doctor Sloper,

Thank you for your letter. I understand you very well.

You love your daughter. I love my brother, but I understand him too. He thinks only about himself. I know that. Morris is clever, but he does not want to work. I am poor, but sometimes I have to give him money.

Yours sincerely,

Mary Montgomery

Doctor Sloper told Catherine about his meeting with Morris Townsend. And he told her about Mrs Montgomery's letter.

After that, Catherine did not speak to her father for a week. But she did not meet Morris. She was very unhappy. She wanted to be a good daughter to her father. But she wanted to marry Morris Townsend.

Catherine was a patient young woman.

'I will wait,' she thought. 'I will change Father's mind. It will not happen quickly. But it *will* happen!'

Catherine wrote a letter to Morris Townsend.

Washington Square
February, 1847

Dear Morris,

Please be patient. I have not changed my mind about you. I love you and I want to marry you. But we must wait and I must think about everything.
I want to obey my father. He is a good man. But he does not understand you.
I do love you, Morris. Please believe that.

From your friend,
Catherine Sloper

Catherine's aunt, Lavinia Penniman, liked Morris Townsend very much. She wrote to him every day. She gave him news about Catherine. Mrs Penniman wanted Catherine to marry the young man. Morris did not go to the house in Washington Square. But sometimes Mrs Penniman met him secretly.

One day, Mrs Penniman told Morris about a plan. It was her own plan. She had not told Catherine about it.

'Catherine loves you, Morris,' she said. 'You must marry her secretly! Tell her father about it afterwards. I will help you.'

Morris was worried. 'This woman is a fool,' he thought. 'She will make trouble for me.' But he did not say anything.

'You are a good man,' Mrs Penniman said. 'You want Catherine, not her money. I know that.'

'I want some money too,' said Morris. He smiled at Catherine's aunt. 'Catherine is afraid of her father. I don't want to make her unhappy. But I don't want her to be poor.'

'And my brother doesn't want his daughter to be unhappy,' said Mrs Penniman. 'I'm sure about that. You must marry her, Morris. Then the doctor will help both of you.'

'No! We must wait,' Morris replied. 'Catherine is patient and I will be patient too. Please tell her that.'

———

That evening, Mrs Penniman told Catherine about her meeting with Morris. And she told the young woman about her plan.

Catherine was angry with her.

'I am afraid of my father, Aunt Lavinia,' she said. 'I must obey him. You must not meet Morris secretly. You will make trouble for us. Please don't meet him again!'

Mrs Penniman was very unhappy.

'You are very unkind to me, Catherine,' she said. 'I was trying to help you.'

'Please, Aunt Lavinia,' Catherine said. 'I want to be alone. I must think quietly.'

7

Father and Daughter

Mrs Penniman left the sitting-room and she went to her bedroom. Catherine sat alone by the fire in the sitting-room. Soon, it was eleven o'clock and the big house was very quiet.

At last, Catherine stood up. She went to the door of her father's library. She knocked on the door but she did not open it. She was afraid.

Doctor Sloper opened the door.

'What is wrong, Catherine?' he asked. 'Why are you standing there?'

Catherine did not answer. Her father went to his desk. He began to write.

After a minute, Catherine spoke.

'I want to tell you something, Father,' she said. 'I have not spoken to Mr Townsend for more than three weeks.'

'Have you written to him?' the doctor asked quickly. 'Are you still engaged to him?'

'I sent him a letter,' Catherine said. 'I asked Morris to wait for me. We are still engaged.'

Suddenly, Doctor Sloper stood up and kissed his daughter.

'Do you want to make me happy, Catherine?' he asked.

'Yes, Father,' she replied.

'Listen to me,' the doctor said. 'I know about life. I know about young men. Some of them are bad. Some of them tell lies! You must end this engagement, Catherine. Tell Mr Townsend that.'

'Mr Townsend is *not* bad,' Catherine said. 'He does not tell lies. I will *not* end our engagement. I want to be happy, Father.'

'Very well, Catherine,' her father said coldly. He sat down at his desk again.

'I want to meet Morris again. Do you agree to that?' Catherine asked.

'No! I don't agree to it!' the doctor replied.

'I *will* marry him,' Catherine said. 'Will you forgive me, Father?'

'No! Never!' said Doctor Sloper.

'Father! Please talk to Morris again,' Catherine said. 'He is a good man. You will change your mind about him.'

'No! I will never speak to Mr Townsend again,' the doctor replied. 'And I will never change my mind. Tell him that! You want to marry him. Very well! Marry him now. Or marry him after my death. But Mr Townsend will never have my money. I'll give it to a hospital. Tell him that, Catherine!'

'I love you, Father,' Catherine said. 'I will always love you. But I am going to marry Morris!'

'You are a cruel, unkind child,' the doctor said. 'You will make your old father very unhappy.'

Catherine started to cry. She held out her hands towards her father. He got up from his desk and led her to the door. Then he pushed Catherine out of the room and closed the door behind her.

Doctor Sloper listened carefully. Catherine was standing outside the door and she was crying quietly. But at last, she walked away.

Then the doctor smiled.

'Catherine is *not* weak,' he said to himself. 'I am surprised! She is not going to end her engagement to that young man.' And he laughed quietly.

———

The next morning, the doctor spoke to his sister, Lavinia Penniman.

'Please do not meet Mr Townsend again, Lavinia,' he said. 'Do not help him. Do not speak to him. Do not write to him. I don't want any of that young man's friends in my house!'

'You are very unkind, Austin,' Mrs Penniman said. 'You are cruel to me. And you are very cruel to your daughter. Catherine did not sleep last night. She was crying all night.'

'Catherine is a healthy young woman. A night without sleep will not hurt her,' the doctor replied.

Mrs Penniman left the room quickly.

———

Later that day, Catherine wrote to Morris Townsend again.

Dear Morris,

Please come here tomorrow afternoon. I have some important news. I must see you. I will tell you everything then.

Catherine

———

Morris came to the house in Washington Square the next afternoon. Doctor Sloper was not at home. The young man held Catherine in his arms.

'I have not seen you for more than three weeks, Catherine,' he said. 'Have you made your choice now?'

'My choice?' Catherine asked. 'What choice?'

'The choice between me and your father,' replied Morris. 'You cannot make us both happy. You must choose one of us, Catherine. You must choose now.'

'Oh, Morris! I choose you,' Catherine said.

'Will you marry me next week?' the young man asked.

'Next week?' Catherine was suddenly afraid. 'We can't get married next week, Morris. We must wait!'

'Why must we wait?' the young man said. 'What are we waiting *for*? Ah, Catherine! You are afraid of your father. You do not love me. You are very weak.'

'No! I am strong!' said Catherine. 'I will wait for you Morris. I will change my father's mind.'

'No, Catherine. You won't change his mind,' Morris said angrily. 'Your father will always hate me. Marry me now, Catherine!'

'Yes. We'll get married now,' said the young woman sadly. 'But I will never have my father's money. He will give all his money to a hospital.'

Suddenly, the young woman smiled. 'But the money isn't important,' she said. 'We will have each other. We will always love each other, Morris. And I have some money from my mother – ten thousand dollars.

Yes, Morris. I will marry you next week.'

For a moment, Morris did not speak. Then he put his arms around Catherine again.

'My dear, good girl,' he said. 'We will get married – soon. But I must go now.'

A few minutes later, Morris Townsend was walking towards his sister's house. He was thinking.

'Only ten thousand dollars!' he thought. 'It isn't very much. Catherine will never have her father's money. Do I want a plain, uninteresting wife with only ten thousand dollars? I must have some money soon. But is ten thousand dollars enough?'

8

Doctor Sloper's Plan

The big red house in Washington Square was not a happy place. Doctor Sloper did not speak to Catherine. He did not look at her. And for several days, she did not speak to him.

Then one evening, the unhappy young woman went to her father's library.

'I have spoken to Mr Townsend, Father,' she said. 'We will get married soon. And before that, we will meet once every week.'

'Why are you telling me this?' the doctor asked coldly. 'I'm not interested in you or in Townsend.'

Catherine left the room sadly.

Then Doctor Sloper suddenly thought of a plan. He spoke to his daughter about it the next day.

'When are you going to get married, Catherine?' he asked. 'Will you get married before September?'

'I don't know, Father,' Catherine replied. 'Morris hasn't told me.'

'Please wait for six months,' the doctor said. 'I will take you to Europe. You must see more of the world before your marriage. We will have a holiday together. We will leave soon. We will be in Europe for six months. After that, you will get married.'

Catherine did not want to leave New York City. She did not want to leave Morris. But she wanted to make her father happy.

'I'll come to Europe with you, Father,' she said.

———

The next day, Catherine met Morris Townsend and told him about her father's plan.

'I will go with him, but I won't be happy in Europe,' she said. 'I don't want to leave you, Morris.'

'But there are many beautiful things in Europe, Catherine,' said Morris. 'There are fine buildings and beautiful paintings. Don't you want to see them?'

'Oh, no,' Catherine replied. 'I'm not interested in those things.'

'She is a very boring young woman!' Morris thought. 'Do I want to marry her?'

'I understand Father's plan,' Catherine said. 'He wants me to forget you. But I *won't* forget you!'

Morris laughed.

'Don't worry, my dear,' he said. 'Go to Europe. Buy your wedding clothes in Paris. After six months, you will be back in New York. We will be married in six months' time.'

'But we will not see each other for six months,' Catherine said sadly. 'That is a long time.'

'You will have six months alone with your father,' Morris replied. 'Be clever. Use the time well. Change his mind about me. Change his mind about the money. We must not lose the money!'

'Yes, I will try to change his mind,' said Catherine. 'Will you always love me, Morris?'

'I will love you more every day,' the young man replied. He smiled at Catherine and he kissed her.

———

A week later, Catherine and her father left for Europe. The night before their journey, Mrs Penniman had spoken quietly to Catherine.

'I will take care of Morris for you,' she had said. 'Don't worry about him.'

———

It was spring in New York. Mrs Penniman liked being in the house in Washington Square. She was happy there without her brother. She often invited Morris Townsend to the house. Morris sat in the doctor's library. He sat in the doctor's chair and he smoked the doctor's cigars.

Morris wrote to Catherine twice every month. But Mrs Penniman always wrote the address on the envelopes. She did not want her brother to see the young man's letters.

9

Europe

The spring was beautiful in Europe. Doctor Sloper took his daughter to England, to France, and then to Switzerland. They saw many fine buildings and many beautiful paintings. Catherine wanted to make her father happy. She looked at all these things. But she was not interested in them. She was only interested in Morris Townsend's letters. She read them again and again. And she replied to them secretly.

Six months passed. It was the end of September. The Slopers were in Switzerland.

One day, they were walking in the mountains. In the late afternoon, Catherine was tired. She sat down and rested. Her father walked on.

Catherine was thinking about Morris Townsend. He was thousands of miles away. She was very lonely without him.

Doctor Sloper had walked back to his daughter. Suddenly, he was standing in front of her. She looked up at him.

'You are thinking about that young man,' the doctor said. 'Have you ended your engagement?'

'No, Father,' Catherine said quietly.

'Does Townsend write to you?' the doctor asked.

'Yes, he writes to me twice every month,' she replied.

'I'm very angry with you,' the doctor said. 'You have made me very unhappy. And I am a hard man, Catherine. You will not get any of my money!'

'I'm sorry, Father,' Catherine replied. 'I don't want you to be unhappy. But why are you saying these things now?'

'I have been thinking these things for six months,' the doctor replied angrily. 'You are a very foolish girl. Morris Townsend will spend all your money. Then he will leave you!'

'That's not true!' Catherine said.

'It *is* true, but you won't believe it,' said Doctor Sloper. 'We will go back to our hotel now. But we are going to stay in Europe for another six months!'

Catherine was worried, but she did not say anything. She did not understand her father.

———

In March 1848, the Slopers were returning to America at last. One evening, they were sitting in a hotel in Liverpool, in England. The next day, their ship was going to start its journey to New York. The Slopers had finished their dinner. Catherine stood up.

'I will go to bed now, Father,' she said. 'I'm very tired.'

'Catherine! We will be in New York soon,' Doctor Sloper said in a cold voice. 'What are you going to do about Townsend?'

'Morris and I will get married,' Catherine replied.

'Does he still write to you?' asked the doctor.

45

'Oh, yes, Father,' said Catherine. 'Yes. He writes beautiful letters.'

'And does he write about marriage?' asked Doctor Sloper.

'Yes, he writes about our marriage in every letter,' Catherine replied.

'Will you marry him immediately?' asked the doctor.

'I cannot answer you now,' said his daughter. 'I must speak to Mr Townsend about our plans.'

Doctor Sloper smiled.

'You have been in Europe for a year, Catherine,' he said. 'You have seen many beautiful things. You have learnt many things. But you still want to marry that young man. Foolish girl! Marry him! You will not be happy.'

After that, the doctor did not speak about Morris Townsend again.

10

Catherine and Morris Meet Again

Lavinia Penniman was very happy. Catherine was at home again.

'I have met dear Morris many times,' she told the young woman. 'He is a very clever and interesting young man. And he still loves you very much.'

'You have been very kind, Aunt Lavinia,' Catherine said.

'I wanted to help you both, my dear,' Mrs Penniman said. 'I wanted Morris to be happy in this house. I often invited him here. He often sat in your father's library.'

Catherine was very surprised, but she did not reply.

'And I have some good news,' Mrs Penniman said. 'Morris has a job now. He works in an office.'

'Oh, Aunt Lavinia, I'm very happy about that,' said Catherine.

'Your father will change his mind about dear Morris now,' said her aunt.

'No! Father will never change his mind,' said Catherine. 'But that's not important now. Morris has a job. We will be married soon. Morris was worried about Father's money. He wanted me to have it. But the money isn't important.'

'You are very brave, Catherine,' said Mrs Penniman. 'But you mustn't forget about the money. It *is* important. You must speak to your father again.'

'Why do you say that?' Catherine said. 'Last year, you did not want me to obey my father. Now you have changed your mind. Well, *I* don't want to obey him now. I don't care about him. I'm going to marry Morris.'

—

Morris Townsend visited the house in Washington Square the next day.

'I'm happy to see you again, Catherine,' the young man said.

'I'm happy too,' Catherine replied.

'He is very handsome,' she thought. 'And I love him very much.'

Morris asked Catherine many questions about Europe. He asked her about the buildings and the paintings. She could not answer any of his questions.

'I have forgotten about Europe,' she said. 'I was thinking about you all the time. Now I am home again, and we can get married.'

'Has your father changed his mind about me?' the young man asked.

'No! But I don't care,' said Catherine. 'We can live without his money.'

'My dear girl! This is not right,' said Morris. 'I am a proud man. Your father must not think bad things about his son-in-law. I must change his mind!'

'No! Please don't speak to him,' Catherine said sadly. 'My father hates you. He hates me too. At last, I understand him. He has never loved me. He loved my mother. *She* was clever and beautiful. I am not clever and I am not beautiful. My father is a hard, cruel man. He will never help us.'

'I don't understand your family, Catherine!' Morris said angrily.

'Please don't be angry,' Catherine replied. 'Please be kind to me. *You* are my family now.'

Morris held Catherine in his arms and he kissed her.

'My dear, good girl,' he said. Then he left the room. He was going to leave the house.

Mrs Penniman was standing in the hall. She saw Morris Townsend's face.

'What is wrong, Morris?' she asked him.

'I can't marry Catherine,' he said. 'I must go away from this city!'

49

11

'I Am a Proud Man'

Morris Townsend visited the house in Washington Square several more times. But his visits were very short. Catherine did not understand the reason for this. She did not know about his words to her aunt.

'Soon, Morris will marry me and I will be happy,' she said to herself.

One afternoon, Morris and Catherine were drinking tea.

'You are very pale today, Morris,' Catherine said. 'Are you ill?'

'Yes. I am working too much,' Morris replied. 'But I must work all the time. We cannot live on your money. I am a proud man!'

'But I want to marry you, Morris,' Catherine said.

Morris walked quickly round and round the room.

'Catherine,' he said. 'I – I must have more money. I'm going to work in New Orleans. But I can't take you with me.'

'New Orleans? Why are you going to work in New Orleans?' Catherine asked.

'I will earn more money there,' Morris replied. 'I *must* earn more money. We will get married later.'

'But I have money, Morris,' Catherine said. 'Don't think about money all the time. Think about me! Think about our marriage! Why must we wait?'

Morris became angry.

'Stop asking all these questions!' he shouted. 'I must go now. I'm very busy.'

'When will you come again?' Catherine asked.

'I'll come on Saturday,' Morris replied.

'No! Come tomorrow,' said Catherine. 'Please come tomorrow.'

'No! I will be busy tomorrow,' said Morris. 'I'll come on Saturday.' He walked towards the door.

But Catherine ran across the room and stood in front of the door.

'Please come tomorrow, Morris,' she said quietly.

'Catherine, you are making me angry,' Morris said. His voice was cold. 'I'll go now.'

Catherine moved away from the door.

'You're going to leave me for ever,' she said. 'Why? What have I done? Why have you changed you mind?'

'I'll write to you,' said Morris.

Catherine started to cry. 'You will never come here again,' she said sadly.

'Dear Catherine, you will see me again soon,' Morris said. Then he left the room and he left the house.

———

Catherine was lying on a sofa in the sitting-room. She was crying quietly. She had been crying for a long time. Morris did not love her! He wanted to leave her. She knew that. He had said strange, cruel things to her.

Hours passed and the room became dark. Morris did not return to the house. Catherine heard her father coming home. She did not want to see him. She went quickly to her bedroom.

That evening, Catherine went to the dining-room and sat at the table with her father and her aunt. But she did not eat much. Her father did not look at her. He did not see her pale, unhappy face.

After dinner, her aunt followed Catherine to her bedroom.

'Something is wrong, Catherine,' she said. 'Let me help you, my dear.'

'Nothing is wrong,' Catherine replied. 'I don't want any help. Please, Aunt Lavinia, I want to be alone.'

12

Catherine Is Alone

The next day, Catherine waited at home. But Morris Townsend did not come. The day after, Catherine wrote to him.

Washington Square
Thursday

Dear Morris,

You were cold and cruel to me on Tuesday. I am very unhappy. Please come to me.

Catherine

An hour later, she wrote to him again.

Dear Morris,

I was very foolish on Tuesday. Please forgive me. And please come back to me.

Catherine

Morris did not reply to Catherine's letters.

Days passed. Doctor Sloper watched his daughter carefully. On Sunday, he spoke to his sister.

'Lavinia, that young man has changed his mind,' he said. 'He won't marry my daughter. He has left her for ever.'

'No, no, Austin. That's not true,' Mrs Penniman replied.

'Yes, it *is* true,' said her brother. 'And I am happy about it! I was right about Mr Morris Townsend.'

'Your only daughter is unhappy and you are happy about it,' said Mrs Penniman angrily. 'You are a very cruel man, Austin.'

Mrs Penniman went to Catherine's bedroom. Catherine was sitting by the window. She was looking into the street.

'I'm sorry about your plans. Are you very unhappy, my dear?' her aunt asked.

'No. My plans haven't changed,' Catherine replied.

'But Mr Townsend's plans have changed,' said Mrs Penniman.

'What do you mean?' The unhappy young woman asked quietly. 'What has Morris told you?'

'He told me about your argument,' said her aunt.

'When did you speak to him? Where is he? You must tell me!' Catherine said.

She started to cry. 'Oh, why don't you leave us alone! You have spoilt everything!'

'You are unkind, Catherine,' said Mrs Penniman. 'I tried to help you.'

'Morris has left me,' said Catherine. 'He told you about it. But he did not tell me!'

'He will come back, my dear,' said her aunt.

'No. He will not come back,' said Catherine.

———

Two days later, Catherine received a letter. Morris Townsend had left New York. He was far away, in another city.

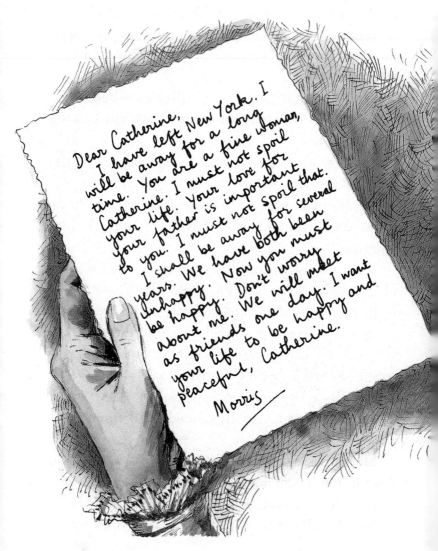

Dear Catherine, New York. I
I have left New York. I
will be away for a long
time. You are a fine woman,
Catherine. I must not spoil
your life. Your love for
your father is important
to you. I must not spoil that.
I shall be away for several
years. We have both been
unhappy. Now you must
be happy. Don't worry
about me. We will meet
as friends one day. I want
your life to be happy and
peaceful, Catherine.

Morris

Catherine did not tell her father about this letter. But a week later, he asked her about her plans.

'When are you going to leave the house, Catherine?' he asked. 'When are you going to get married?'

'I'm not going to leave, Father,' she replied coldly.

'Has Townsend ended your engagement?' the doctor asked happily.

'I have ended the engagement, Father,' Catherine replied. 'I will not marry Mr Townsend. He has left New York. I wanted him to leave.'

Doctor Sloper was very surprised.

'What did Mr Townsend think about that?' he asked.

'I don't know!' said Catherine.

'And you don't care!' said Doctor Sloper. 'You are a cruel young woman, Catherine!'

The doctor laughed and he walked away.

13

The Years Pass

Catherine did not tell anybody the truth about Morris Townsend. Her life went on, but one part of her had died. Once, the unhappy young woman had loved Morris Townsend. But he had lied to her. Once, she had loved her father. But she did not love him any more. He had been right about Morris, but he had been cruel.

The years passed. Two other men wanted to marry Catherine. But she did not want to get married.

———

In 1864, Catherine was thirty-nine years old, and her father was nearly seventy. One day, the doctor had some news for Catherine.

'Morris Townsend is here in New York City again,' he said. 'He was married, but his wife has died. Now he is waiting for *my* death. Then he will try to marry you. Make me a promise, Catherine. You must not marry him! Promise me that.'

'I won't promise you anything,' Catherine said.

'I shall give all my money to a hospital,' said Doctor Sloper angrily.

———

A year later, Doctor Sloper died. He did give most of his money to a hospital in the city. He also gave some money to his two sisters. But he did not give anything

58

to his daughter.

Before his death, Dr Sloper wrote to Mrs Almond.

> My daughter has her mother's money. She does not spend it. I don't want any man to marry her for money. I will not give her any of my money.

Mrs Penniman was surprised and unhappy about the doctor's money. But Catherine did not care about her father or his money.

'I'm happy without father's money,' she said. 'And I shall never marry.'

―――

Another year passed. One evening in July 1866, Catherine and her Aunt Lavinia were in the sitting-room in the house at Washington Square. The weather was very hot. Catherine was sewing and Mrs Penniman was reading a book.

'I saw Morris Townsend today, Catherine,' Lavinia Penniman said.

Catherine stopped sewing. She sat very still.

'How is he?' she said after a few moments.

'He wants to talk to you,' said her aunt. 'He loves you. He has always loved you.'

'Please don't say that, Aunt,' Catherine said. 'I don't want to speak about him.'

'You are a cruel woman,' said Mrs Penniman.

It was dark in the room and the old lady did not see the tears running down Catherine's face.

14

'I Have Never Forgotten You'

Mrs Penniman wanted Catherine to meet Morris Townsend. She wanted them to be friends again. She wanted them to get married. But Catherine did not want to talk about Morris. She did not want to think about him.

One evening, the two women were in the sitting-room. Catherine was sewing.

Suddenly, Mrs Penniman spoke.

'Catherine, listen to me!' she said. 'Morris is going to leave New York soon. But he wants to talk to you. Please meet him.'

'No!' said Catherine. 'I don't want to meet him. Please tell him that!'

But at that moment, the doorbell rang. Catherine stood up quickly. She looked at her aunt.

'Aunt Lavinia,' she said angrily. 'Did you —?'

A servant opened the sitting-room door, and Morris Townsend entered the room. Mrs Penniman went out quickly.

Catherine and Morris looked at each other. Morris was forty-five years old. He was no longer handsome. He was fat and he had a beard. His eyes were cold.

'I want us to be friends, Catherine,' he said. 'I have never forgotten you. Do you hate me? Can we forget the past?'

'No, I don't hate you,' Catherine replied. 'But I don't want to talk to you. I cannot forget the past.'

'You have never married,' Morris said.

'No. I did not want to marry,' Catherine replied. 'Please go now. I don't want to see you again.'

'I'm sorry, Catherine,' Morris said. 'Goodbye.'

———

He left the room and closed the door behind him. Mrs Penniman was waiting for him in the hall.

'You were wrong,' Morris said to her. 'She doesn't love me. She has never loved me. But she didn't marry. Why not?'

'Oh, she *does* love you,' the old woman said. 'You must be patient. Will you come here again?'

'No! Never!' said Morris Townsend. He left the house. The front door closed behind him.

In the sitting-room, Catherine began sewing again.

Published by Macmillan Heinemann ELT
Between Towns Road, Oxford OX4 3PP
Macmillan Heinemann ELT is an imprint of
Macmillan Publishers Limited
Companies and representatives throughout the world
Heinemann is a registered trademark of Harcourt Education, used under licence.

ISBN 1–405072–55–5
EAN 978–1–405072–55–7

This retold version by Margaret Tarner for Macmillan Readers
First published 1999
Text © Margaret Tarner 1999, 2002, 2005
Design and illustration © Macmillan Publishers Limited 1999, 2002, 2005

This edition first published 2005

Illustrated by Shirley Bellwood
Map on page 3 by Peter Harper
Original cover template design by Jackie Hill
Cover illustration by Getty/Bridgeman
Acknowledgements: The publishers would like to thank Mary Evans
Picture Library for permission to reproduce the picture on page 4.

Printed in Thailand

2009 2008 2007 2006 2005
10 9 8 7 6 5 4 3 2 1